Big Bombers

Strategic Air Command's B-52s, Swingwings, and Stealth

Robert F. Dorr

Jim Benson

Motorbooks International
Publishers & Wholesalers ®

First published in 1989 by Motorbooks International Publishers & Wholesalers Inc, P O Box 2, 729 Prospect Avenue, Osceola, WI 54020 USA

Printed and bound in Hong Kong

The information in this book is true and complete to the best of our knowledge. All recommendations are made without any guarantee on the part of the author or publisher, who also disclaim any liability incurred in connection with the use of this data or specific details

Library of Congress Cataloging-in-Publication Data
Dorr, Robert F.
    Big bombers / Robert F. Dorr, Jim Benson.
        p.   cm.
    ISBN 0-87938-374-7 (soft)
    1. Bombers—United States—Pictorial works.
I. Benson, Jim, 1960-   II. Title.
UG1242.B6D66   1989   89-9255
358.4'2'0973—dc20   CIP

Motorbooks International books are also available at discounts in bulk quantity for industrial or sales-promotional use. For details write to Special Sales Manager at the Publisher's address

The views expressed in this book are the authors' and do not necessarily reflect those of the Department of State or of the United States Air Force.

Jim Benson
Great Falls, Montana
Robert F. Dorr
Oakton, Virginia

On the front cover: High-tech bombers demand high-tech maintenance. The bright yellow hoses duct conditioned air to the sensitive electronics and avionics systems of this B-1B. *Jim Benson*

On the frontispiece: War in the twenty-first century may look like this. Dark, brooding shapes moving along the runway to start their mission. A pair of Rockwell B-1B Excalibur bombers (86-0110 and 86-0111) belonging to the 319th Bomb Wing taxi out for the morning flight at Grand Forks AFB, North Dakota, on 16 August 1988. The B-1B has received its share of criticism, but SAC crews are pleased with the swing-wing, supersonic bomber and are flying it seriously. As of 31 January 1988, these particular B-1B bombers had logged, respectively, 54.9 and 104.0 airframe flying hours. *Jim Benson*

On the title page: A dark silhouette in the evening, B-52H Stratofortress 60-0015 lands at Fairchild AFB, Washington on 23 May 1988 with the aid of the braking parachute. To reduce strain on landing gear brakes, Air Force aircraft are always required to use the braking parachute when one is provided. *Jim Benson*

On the back cover: It always is, always was, people. GARGOYLE, or First Lieutenant Russell J. Megargle, navigator extraordinaire, is an excellent symbol of all the people who fly big bombers as he prepares to close the hatch. His FB-111A will go. *Lieutenant Cara Mason*

On the contents page: Aircraft 68-0118 has swept its wings back for high-speed flight. When flying on an actual combat mission, the B-1B is literally faster than a speeding bullet. *Jim Benson*

With affection and respect, this volume is dedicated to the brave men and women who serve as Strategic Air Command boom operators—who do it backward and make it happen—and especially to the boomers who helped with this book: SGT Lee Deibert, A1C Ursula Erquitt, TSGT Dennis C. Fox,

Contents

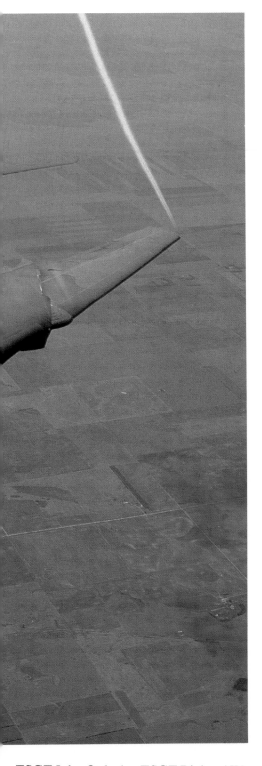

TSGT John Oglesby, TSGT Richard W. Otis, SGT Russell Sikes.

As Fox puts it, "We've got a $64 million airplane which weighs more than half a million pounds with two college boys and a flight engineer to keep it in the air, and it's all so that I can go to work."

Captain Tom McAusland's *A Wing An' 10 Prayers* close up. *Jim Benson*

Acknowledgments

Even a modest look at the Strategic Air Command's bomber force would have been impossible without assistance from many people. Any errors are the sole responsibility of the authors, but if there should be any credit, it belongs to many in and out of SAC who made this work possible.

Assistance in the preparation of this work was provided by the Department of State, Headquarters United States Air Force, Headquarters Strategic Air Command and a number of SAC bases. The authors owe a very special debt to Major Suzanne Randle at SAC Headquarters and Captain Jay De Frank in the Pentagon who helped to make this book a reality.

We also want to acknowledge our debt to:

At Barksdale AFB, Louisiana: Captain John Lahmon and A1C Stephen Pierce, Public Affairs; Harold D. (Buck) Rigg and Milaine J. Monday, Eighth Air Force Museum; Captain Leeroy Martin, KC-10 instructor pilot.

At Fairchild AFB, Washington: Captain Brad Peck, 1LT Terry Francisco and MSGT Ron Pack, Public Affairs; Lt. Col. Jack Gotcher; Captain Nick Islin, Captain Don Dunbar, Captain Greg Lenhart, and Lt. Col. Don Cook, SAC crew members.

At Grand Forks AFB, North Dakota: Captain Barbara Claypool, Public Affairs; Captain Richard Witt, B-1B aircraft commander.

At Malmstrom AFB, Montana: Captain Don Planalp, Public Affairs.

At Minot AFB, North Dakota: Captain Oscar Searra and Sergeant Gene Ladoucer Public Affairs, and CMSGT Fred Gantzer, Chief of Maintenance.

At Plattsburgh AFB, New York: 1Lt Cara Mason, Captain Alan Gregory, 2LT Casey S. Mahon, TSGT Annette Crawford and TSGT John F. Gardner, Public Affairs; Lt. Col. John Plantikow, FB-111A pilot.

In the Pentagon: Colonel Preston R. Olinger and Lt. Col. Lawrence R. Nilssen, B-52 pilots.

Among the fraternity: Joseph G. Handelman DDS, Don Logan, Peter Mancus, Donald S. McGarry, R. J. Mills Jr, Lindsay T. Peacock, Major Brian C. Rogers, Bryan Wilburn and "The gang at Roy's."

Sinister, perhaps, to those who might threaten the American heartland, but a thing of beauty to the men who fly it, Boeing B-52H Stratofortress 61-0039 of the 92nd Bomb Wing sits on alert on 24 May 1988, with a full load of cruise missiles. The AGM-86B air-launched cruise missile, is the latest of an encyclopedic range of bombs, rockets, mines, missiles and other weaponry carried by the venerable B-52 over many, many years. The cruise missile can be launched while the bomber is still a considerable distance from target, sparing the B-52 crew any need to fly straight into an enemy's heaviest defenses. *Jim Benson*

B-52 in action

Almost every airplane is newer. Many fly faster. Most are better looking. There exists scarcely a single aircraft—anywhere—which is less comfortable to climb into, to strap into, to fly.

Old, slow, uncomfortable, the Boeing B-52 Stratofortress might not be worth mentioning except, of course, that it is the longest-serving warplane of all time, is among history's most important airplanes and remains, on the eve of the 1990s, the backbone of Strategic Air Command's (SAC) bomber force.

Standing in a drizzle at Fairchild Air Base twelve miles west-southwest of Spokane, it evokes a chill, a pause of breath, a little flicker of awe, to watch crews grinding the Stratofortress through its paces only feet off the ground, where one tiny mistake can spell disaster. The Buff, or Big Ugly Fat Fellow, weighs a hundred tons. When you watch it come in, heavy and graceless, you realize that while rehearsing landings and takeoffs the pilot could, oh so easily, dip a wing or drag the ground, bringing collision and sudden death. But it never happens. The Buff seems to hang on its exhaust trails, close enough to the ground to touch, but no contact ever takes place.

Not all flying by the Strategic Air Command occurs around its home bases and not all of it is easy for the general public to take. On one SAC officer's car, there is a bumper sticker: "SEE THE JETS? HEAR THE NOISE? GET USED TO IT." About mid-way through the very long service career of the B-52 Stratofortress, it became abundantly clear that SAC would have to shift the focus of its war-fighting preparations from high altitude down to treetop level—and that the American public would, indeed, have to get used to it. You must train as you will fight. SAC *must* fly its Stratofortresses at low altitude whether or not the public really believes that jet engine noise is the sound of freedom.

On 29 June 1955, SAC's first B-52 Stratofortress arrived at Castle AFB, California. It was flown from the Boeing plant in Seattle by 93rd Bomb Wing skipper, Brigadier General William E. Eubank. Powered by eight Pratt & Whitney J57 turbojet engines developing 10,000 lb of thrust each (and generating the dirtiest, blackest smoke trails ever to emanate from any warplane until the water-injected engines were replaced by TF33 turbofans on the B-52H), the silvery new B-52
continued on page 10

continued from page 9
bomber was capable of attacking targets as far away as 7,500 miles, giving SAC a real global capability at jet speeds.

In January 1957, Fifteenth Air Force commander, Major General Archie Old, led three B-52 Stratofortresses on an around-the-world flight, refueled aloft by KC-97 tankers, demonstrating global capability.

In early years of the B-52's career, the mighty bomber could penetrate Soviet air space at high altitude and drop one of the monster atomic bombs (which, in those days, each side seemed to be making bigger and bigger). All of this changed with the development of the surface-to-air missile (SAM), unveiled for the world so dramatically with the Soviet downing of a U-2 spy plane on 1 May 1960. With the advent of the SAM, and other sophisticated defenses found in today's world, flying high-altitude strategic bombing missions became nearly *continued on page 12*

Coming in to take on fuel from a KC-135A tanker, the crew of this ominous-looking B-52H Stratofortress demonstrates the important function of mid-air refueling, a kind of revolution which has stretched SAC's legs around the world. When it first entered service in 1955, the B-52 had to throttle back in order to "gas up" from the prop-driven KC-97. The advent of a jet tanker changed all that. *Jim Benson*

continued from page 10
suicidal. And free-fall gravity
bombs became obsolete.

SAC's strategic planners
adapted by switching the role of
the B-52 to low-altitude
penetration. And their weapon of
choice switched to air-launched
cruise missiles (ALCM), which
allow the crews to "stand-off"—
allowing the crew its best chance
of survival. It is a tribute to the
B-52 that the aircraft was
adaptable enough for the transition
from high- to low-altitude
warfare.

Today, the Stratofortress can
still carry gravity bombs.
Additional details about these
weapons are not usually given
publicity.

In any event, it is the standoff
weapon rather than the gravity
bomb that makes the B-52
Stratofortress so fearsome to
potential enemies. Over its long
life, the Stratofortress has been
modified to carry three principal
standoff weapons. The first was the
North American AGM-28 (GAM-
77) Hound Dog ALCM, capable of
carrying a nuclear warhead, which
entered service 21 December
1959. Each B-52 could carry two
forty-three-foot Hound Dogs, and
could launch them when the
bomber was 500 miles from target.
The Hound Dog had an unusual
feature in that its jet engine could
be used to augment the thrust of
the B-52's engines during takeoff.
It remained in service until 1975.

In the category of "things
under wings," the B-52 was also
equipped to carry the McDonnell
GAM-72 (later ADM-20) Quail, a
"decoy" missile designed to
confuse and confound enemy
defenses while the bomber sped
onward to its target. Powered by a
single J85 turobjet engine, Quail
eventually served in fourteen
squadrons. Though barely twelve
feet in length, it could fool an
enemy's radar into thinking that it
was a B-52, giving off a fake radar
cross-section and infrared
"signature" to cause the adversary
to waste resources trying to shoot
it down.

More recent is the Boeing
AGM-69A SRAM (short-range
attack missile) with potential for a
nuclear warhead. Delivered to
SAC's 42nd Bomb Wing at Loring
AFB, Maine, on 4 March 1972, the
14 foot SRAM (also employed by
the FB-111A) can be air-launched
some thirty-five to one hundred
continued on page 14

A sky full of Buffs. These "Big Ugly
Fat Fellows," as B-52s are
affectionately called, are working out
near day's end at Fairchild AFB,
Washington, home of the 92nd Bomb
Wing, on 23 May 1988. The ability to
take off in rapid succession is vitally
important in any scenario for a
nuclear war, since SAC bases could
come under attack from submarine-
launched missiles with only minutes'
notice. In an actual combat situation,
B-52s would launch one behind the
other, ignoring the usual safety rules
in order to get as much of the force
aloft as possible. *Jim Benson*

continued from page 12
miles from target, giving the bomber crew the opportunity to avoid direct harm from the resulting explosion. Each B-52G and H model aircraft can carry up to twenty of these missiles on wing pylons and on a rotary launcher in the bomb bay.

But the "ultimate" weapon for the B-52 Stratofortress in its earth-shattering nuclear bombing role is the twenty-foot nine-inch Boeing AGM-86B ALCM, the first of which went to the 416th Bomb Wing at Griffiss AFB, New York, on 15 September 1981. Now the bomber crew can launch as far as 1,500 miles from target and the terrain-following missile, rather than the bomber, will have to cope with an enemy's entrenched air defenses. The ALCM (pronounced "al-cum") can carry an atomic warhead.

In the fifties, no one would have thought that the B-52, designed for the atomic mission, would ever be used to drop conventional bombs. In Vietnam, Stratofortresses did just that. In recent years, it was thought to be unlikely again. The B-52, after all, was SAC's *only* strategic bomber (until the arrival of the B-1B). But in 1988, SAC announced changes which gave the B-52 a major role in conventional bombing operations as well as maritime and mining operations.

The dedicated men who fly SAC's B-52 bomber today, all of them younger than the aircraft itself (there have been father and son B-52 pilots), are remarkably skilled and prepared for the nuclear or conventional bombing mission. In wartime, that Stratofortress may fly 4,000 miles to attack a target. The crew may remain in the treetop-altitude, terrain-following mode throughout almost all the mission, relying on EVS (electro-optical viewing system) and terrain-avoidance to prevent them from colliding with a mountain. SAC operates with "hard" crews—the same people stay together—and peacetime preparations for the "real thing" require the greatest of ability and commitment from all of them.

As for the Stratofortress, no words are adequate for the awe that the aircraft and its mission can inspire. Taxiing past B-52G bombers on alert at Barksdale Air Force Base, Louisiana, it was impossible in one breath to ponder the terrible destructiveness of the B-52's mission while, at the same time, marveling at the aerodynamic qualities of the aircraft.

The wing of the B-52 spans 185 feet. Merely to look at how the wing works, even for an experienced pilot, is to evoke more awe. Eight engines slung beneath in pods, in an arrangement first tested on SAC's veteran B-47 Stratojet, the wing "droops" more than fifteen feet to be supported by outrigger wheels while on the ground. In flight, the tips of those wings rise twenty feet moving from the drooping angle to the upstretched position reached while flying. Those who are not engineers wonder how metal can bend so much.

The crew of the B-52 consists of pilot, co-pilot, navigator, radar navigator, Electronic Warfare Officer (EWO) and gunner. The two pilots, navigator and radar navigator can communicate from their side-by-side positions by yelling or gesturing to each other. Otherwise, the crew talks via ICS (intercom system). On nuclear alert, the B-52 may be "buttoned up," with thermal flash curtains closing off all windows, and the crew may fly into combat blind, unable to see outside but relying upon sensors for the safe completion of the mission.

Big, powerful, deadly, the B-52 Stratofortress is more than a warplane: it is a national asset. Even today, when a newer bomber has finally entered service in the form of the B-1B, and the B-2 Stealth bomber may soon follow, the Stratofortress remains vital to the United States and to the Strategic Air Command.

Previous page
Changes in the role of the B-52
bomber, announced by the Air Force
on 11 May 1988, make the
conventional bombing mission more
and more important. At Minot AFB,
North Dakota, on 18 August 1988,
ground crew members work to roll
conventional M117 750 lb bombs
from a "deuce and a half" truck to the
MJ-1 "Jammer" bomb lift, which in
turn will be used to hoist the bombs
aboard B-52H Stratofortress 60-0002
of the 5th Bomb Wing. The blue paint
coating denotes a training weapon not
equipped with a "live" warhead. *Jim
Benson*

"Buff leaves contrails over Idaho," Jim
Benson wrote in his photo log after
watching vapor trails stream back
from B-52H Stratofortress 61-0006 of
the 92nd Bomb Wing flying beneath
his KC-135 tanker high over the
northern heartland of America. Since
the sixties, the demands of warfare
have forced B-52 crews down to
treetop level during combat missions,
since sophisticated defenses are able
to catch any bomber flying up high.
The air refueling mission, however,
carried out while over friendly
territory, must be accomplished at the
higher altitude depicted here. This
Stratofortress is moving into position
to "gas up" from KC-135 boom
operator SGT Russell Sikes. *Jim
Benson*

Wearing the two-tone dark paint scheme which has become *au courrant* for the well-dressed Stratofortress, B-52H 61-0017 of the 92nd Bomb Wing powers up for takeoff at Fairchild AFB, Washington, in the early evening of 23 May 1988. The silhouette of a sea hawk's head is used with permission from the Seattle Seahawks football team. TF33 Turbofan engines on the B-52H are less smoky than the J57 turbojet engines of the B-52G, but some whisps of smoke exhaust are visible nevertheless. *Jim Benson*

In the evening at Fairchild AFB, Washington, a B-52H Stratofortress (61-0009) settles down for the end of a mission. SAC officers are not amused by a popular T-shirt depicting a B-52 crew heading home from a billowing nuclear mushroom cloud and exclaiming, "Now it's Miller time." There is nothing funny about coming home from a mission and all crew members, no matter how eager to see wife and kids, know that scrupulous flying safety procedures must be followed all the way to the end of the flight. *Jim Benson*

The best-known of American jet bombers began its long service career with rather clean contours around its nose. All that changed when a Soviet surface-to-air missile shot down Francis Powers' U-2 spy plane on 1 May 1960, and aerial warfare moved from high altitude to the treetops. B-52H Stratofortress 61-0038 of the 5th Bomb Wing shows the proboscis of today, with ECM (electronic countermeasures) protrusions in front of the windshield and halfway down on the side, EVS (electro-optical viewing system) fairing beneath the right side of the nose, and Rivet Ace FLIR (forward-looking infrared) beneath the left. With all these sensors, B-52H can fly into combat at night and in bad weather. *Jim Benson*

Today's camouflage on the B-52 Stratofortress blends well with the ground—when there's no snow. Aircraft 60-0023 of the 92nd Bomb Wing cruises on 22 May 1988 above rough terrain and white stuff of the sort found throughout major portions of the United States and the Soviet Union. *Jim Benson*

Birth of SAC

Strategic Air Command officially came into existence on 21 March 1946, a year before the US Air Force belatedly became an independent service. In the early years, pushed by General Curtis LeMay (whose name was synonymous with long-range bombing), SAC operated B-29, B-36 and B-50 bombers and, for a brief period, also operated jet fighters in the escort role. SAC's B-29 Superfortresses went to war in the 1950-53 Korean conflict. Not until 1949 did the Soviet Union become the second nation to explode an atomic bomb. The Soviets never did make an investment in a huge bomber force. And until the age of the intercontinental ballistic missile—which is outside our scope—SAC reigned in the skies without serious competition.

The jet age came upon SAC on 23 October 1951, when *continued on page 26*

The most famous bomber of all time and the machine to which SAC owes much of its tradition, the magnificent Boeing B-17 Flying Fortress. Fortresses commanded the skies of Europe, bringing the war home to the Reich at terrible cost to the brave crews who flew and fought in these elegant aircraft. This preserved Fortress is painted to represent B-17G 44-83868. *Robert F. Dorr*

continued from page 25

Colonel Michael McCoy of the 306th Bomb Wing at MacDill AFB, Florida, took delivery of the first Boeing B-47 Stratojet. With rakish swept wings, unique "bicycle" tandem landing gear and fighter-like appearance, the B-47 became SAC's most numerous bomber by 1953, and eventually no fewer than 2,000 of the mighty jets served in the US bomber force. At an air show at Bolling AFB in Washington, DC, in 1954, two Soviet air attaches in full uniform regalia watched in awe as a B-47 demonstrated the "toss bombing" method of delivering an atomic bomb (releasing the bomb while in a climb and veering sharply to escape from the blast). Their eyes popped out.

In some ways, it was an era of innocence. Jimmy Stewart starred in a Hollywood film, *Strategic Air Command*, rich in the patriotic values of a generation that grew up viewing military service as honorable. Other films, like *Bombers B-52* and—a few years later—Rock Hudson's *A Gathering of Eagles* unashamedly depicted clean-cut, clean-living heroes who wanted nothing more than to defend freedom by running the best bomber wing in the Air Force. The B-52 joined the enormous fleet of B-47s, the KC-97 tanker became the standard flight-refueling aircraft, and for a brief period the Convair B-58 Hustler was the fastest thing on wings. The innocence persisted, like the draft, until events in Southeast Asia altered our consciousness forever.

No event in the history of American bombers really has the same significance as the already-mentioned delivery of the first Boeing B-52 Stratofortress into the hands of Brigadier General William E. Eubank of the 93rd Bomb Wing at Castle AFB, California, on 29 June 1955. The eight-engine B-52, a kind of enlarged version of the B-47, was destined to become the longest-serving combat aircraft in world history. When the first Boeing KC-135A Stratotanker made its debut on 28 June 1957 with the same Wing, SAC finally had both a fully intercontinental jet bomber and a jet tanker able to refuel it on long-range missions.

On 1 August 1960, the delta-wing Convair B-58 Hustler—the first supersonic bomber in service anywhere—joined SAC by journeying across the airfield from its production plant to the 43rd Bomb Wing at Carswell AFB, Texas. Beautiful, fast, and a record-setter in every way, the B-58 was also expensive to operate and somewhat short-legged for the strategic mission. It was a flash in the pan, a brilliant and exciting aircraft which was already being removed from service in 1969, barely nine years after beginning its career. Since the experimental XB-70 never did reach SAC, the demise of the Hustler left the B-52 Stratofortress as the only American heavy bomber.

The war in Southeast Asia ushered in a new era for the Strategic Air Command. Having long since divested itself of other duties in order to concentrate on the strategic bombing mission (as well as the land-based intercontinental ballistic missile force), SAC abruptly found itself required to fly and fight in a conventional setting, in a tropical guerrilla war where others were using primitive weapons and fighting a "low-tech" conflict. Having not dropped an iron bomb in anger since Korea, SAC was suddenly tasked to assault Viet Cong jungle redoubts with the mighty B-52.

The Stratofortress raids were code-named Arc Light and they began in 1965 with a disaster, the June collision of two B-52s that killed all aboard. Over time, B-52 *continued on page 31*

The Backbone of the SAC tanker force for many years was the Boeing KC-97 Stratofreighter, itself developed from the B-29. As a propeller-driven aircraft, the KC-97 had to churn mightily through skies to refuel jets, which had to slow down almost to the edge of a stall in order to take on fuel. Now history, KC-97L aircraft 53-0240 basks in the open at Barksdale AFB, Louisiana, on 24 October 1988, awaiting a place in the 8th Air Force Museum operated by curator Buck Rigg. *Robert F. Dorr*

Typical of the World War II bombers which are part of the SAC tradition (though the Strategic Air Command itself was created only in 1946), the Consolidated B-24 Liberator is also the most numerous American warplane ever built. More than 18,000 were manufactured during the war years, although less than half a dozen remain today. Depicted on 24 October 1988, this B-24J Liberator (44-48781), *Laden Maiden*, still needs a nose turret and a rudder panel before being fully restored and placed on display at Barksdale AFB, Louisiana. In the background is the Avro Vulcan bomber also awaiting display. *Robert F. Dorr*

The North American B-45 Tornado, with straight wings and four engines doubled in two nacelles, was the first really practical American jet bomber. SAC operated the Tornado mainly as a reconnaissance aircraft. This "straight" B-45C bomber (48-0010) was operated by the 84th Bomb Squadron, 47th Bomb Wing at RAF Sculthorpe, England, and is seen here in March 1985 just after restoration for the US Air Force Museum in Dayton, Ohio. *David W. Menard*

continued from page 26
operations were tailored for the needs of the conflict, and communist insurgents developed respect for the high-altitude rain of death which could pour upon them from a Stratofortress high overhead. It remained true too often, though, that B-52s were merely bombing rice paddies while fighter-bombers were attacking more lucrative targets in North Vietnam.

From beginning to end of the Vietnam conflict, SAC's KC-135 tankers contributed to the fight, refueling not merely B-52s but virtually every warplane in the combat theater. SAC invested in the "Big Belly" modification program which permitted the B-52D to carry no fewer than 108 500 lb bombs, producing at last a conventional bomber with a truly devastating payload. KC-135s and B-52s remained under SAC jurisdiction rather than that of local commanders. Finally, SAC had a
continued on page 32

The Boeing B-50 Superfortress, based on the wartime B-29, was the last propeller-driven bomber to serve in large numbers with the Strategic Air Command. Many were later converted into tankers and assigned to other commands. This Boeing B-50D Superfortress (49-0389) later became a KB-50J tanker and is now painted to represent an identical aircraft (48-0114) once flown by an officer now serving near its present home, the Dayton, Ohio, Air Museum. *Robert F. Dorr.*

continued from page 31

chance to show its stuff during the Linebacker II operations of 18-29 December 1972, when B-52s were finally unleashed on Hanoi and environs.

The Eleven Days of Christmas, it was called. Bombing restrictions were removed in the North Vietnamese heartland. After years of "limited" war, fully one-third of the worldwide B-52 force gathered at Guam and U-Tapao, Thailand, and assaulted Hanoi in waves. The result was devastation that forced North Vietnam to a settlement. "We won the war in those eleven days," says one SAC officer, "and nobody noticed." The cost: seventeen B-52s lost in combat. B-52 gunners shot down two MiG-21 jets.

Finished with Vietnam duty, the SAC bomber force resumed its status as a nuclear strategic force. The seventies saw the maturing of the General Dynamics FB-111A. Based on the F-111 fighter and originally provided as a kind of a "consolation prize" when a replacement for B-52 seemed unlikely soon, the FB-111A was first delivered to SAC on 8 October 1988, and has been very successful.

At the same time the FB-111A arrived, work began on another attempt to do what had been tried with the XB-70 and seemed to many to be impossible—replace the B-52. In the seventies,

the proposed replacement took the form of the Advanced Manned Strategic Aircraft (AMSA), which became the Rockwell B-1A bomber.

On 5 June 1970, North American (Rockwell) was awarded a development contract to build the new bomber, powered by four huge, 29,900 lb thrust General Electric F101-GE-100 engines. The first B-1A, resplendent in glossy white with a "candy stripe" pitot tube, was rolled out amid much fanfare at Rockwell's Plant 42 in Palmdale, California, on 26 October 1974. For some time thereafter, it seemed certain the B-1A would become the backbone of SAC's bomber force in the eighties. "Nothing stands in the way of the B-1A," proclaimed an Air Staff officer during this era, confident that funding would be forthcoming for the great white bomber.

The end came on 30 June 1977, when President Jimmy Carter announced that the United States would not proceed with *continued on page 35*

The Boeing B-47 Stratojet was the backbone of SAC and a symbol of a nation's strength. In an era when the US was indisputably the dominant force in the world, more than 2,000 Stratojets poured off production lines and stood on guard with atomic payloads. This B-47E (53-2276) is displayed at the Eighth Air Force Museum, Barksdale AFB, Louisiana. *Robert F. Dorr*

The Strategic Air Command is nothing if not people. Smokey (Captain Richard G. Young) and Gargoyle (First Lieutenant Russell J. Megargle) clearly got the idea for helmet-inscribed nicknames—which are not tactical callsigns—from Hollywood's *Top Gun*. If this is life imitating art, it adds *esprit* and it works. Both men belong to the 380th Wing's 528th Bomb Squadron under Lieutenant Colonel Brian A. Arnold. From the camera of Plattsburgh Air Force Base's indefatigable public affairs officer, this view of an FB-111 crew conveys the essence of the men and the mission. *Lieutenant Cara Mason*

The Strategic Air Command, though not conceived for the purpose of bombing guerrilla redoubts in Southeast Asian rain jungles, fought very effectively in Vietnam using first the B-52F and later the B-52D, modified under the "Big Belly" program to carry 108 500 lb bombs. A1C Albert E. Moore, tail gunner of this B-52D Stratofortress (55-0083), *Diamond Lil*, callsign RUBY 3, shot down a MiG-21 fighter over Hanoi during the Christmas Eve 1972 bombings, one of only two B-52 gunners to do so. *Lil* is now displayed at the Air Force Academy in Colorado Springs. *Robert F. Dorr*

The once and future B-52

It grows older. It never grows less impressive. The B-52 Stratofortress looms in the Strategic Air Command picture, still crucial, still irreplaceable. When you talk about the B-52, some things change. Some things never change.

Tall-tail B-52D and F bombers left SAC when reductions in the size of the Stratofortress force began in late 1978. By 1984, when these drawdowns were completed with the retirement of the last eighty B-52Ds, only the current B-52G and H models (with shorter vertical tail fins) remained in the active force.

Yet even today, the Stratofortress remains the most numerous American bomber. Strategic Air Command says it has about 260 Stratofortresses, divided between about 160 B-52G and about 100 B-52H models.

The numbers change, the locations change. What remains constant is that the B-52 is both awe-inspiring and, well, difficult, for the crews who fly this magnificent but discomforting airplane.

On glorious days, when the sun hangs like a red ball on the horizon and the air is glassy and smooth, the mighty Stratofortress is a super ship to fly. The sense of power, of force, of giant wings

scything through the air, can give a man a real dose of the simple sheer joy of flight and make him fiercely proud of his shade 84 blue uniform, his ribbons, his Air Force and country. But most days are other kinds of days. The Stratofortress exists for the grim purpose of war and the joy does not always linger when rehearsing the practical nitty-gritty of nuclear readiness—especially in bad weather.

"I don't think you can say enough about how cramped it is," says one. "And how uncomfortable it is to fly. At low level, it's bumpy, it's hot. Except for pilot and co-pilot, the flying we do around airfields—the pattern work, making touch and go landings—is excruciating. Transition work (practice landings) is just no fun for the guys who aren't sitting up front."

The B-52 is a "huge behemoth of a device," to use the words of pilot Colonel Preston Olinger. A pilot who comes to the Stratofortress direct from UPT (undergraduate pilot training) can say, accurately, that the *wingtank* of a B-52 weighs 6,000 lb more than the airplane he has just finished flying. The airplane, with its familiar wrinkled fuselage sides,

continued on page 44

continued from page 43
has enough metal to make 10,000 garbage cans. The wiring in the Stratofortress is equivalent to five miles of baling wire. Its engines are as powerful as eight locomotives. "And that's the way it flies," says Olinger, "like eight locomotives pulling ten thousand garbage cans with five miles of baling wire."

Strategic Air Command people began pulling alert on 1 October 1957. For three decades, twenty-four hours a day, 365 days a year, they've stood ready to fly and fight on a moment's notice. In earlier years, airborne alert missions involved flying around in "chrome dome" (white and silver) B-52s. Now, the bombers are going through a second generation of camouflage and the alert mission begins at runway's end. But—mindful of how quickly Soviet missiles can arrive at US bases—crews remain ready for "group gaggle" (mass takeoffs) the instant the Klaxon sounds.

continued on page 47

Hauling through North American skies on 27 September 1983 en route toward a rendezvous with a tanker, Boeing B-52H Stratofortress (60-0057) shows the paint scheme with which these bombers were adorned until very recently. Nowadays the red, white and blue of the national insignia has given way to a more subdued version, but the pride remains as if nothing had changed. Bumper sticker at a SAC base: "These colors don't run." *Lindsay T. Peacock*

continued from page 44

The purpose of minimum-interval takeoffs (MITOs), of course, is to get the Stratofortresses aloft as quickly as possible so they won't be destroyed on the ground. SAC routinely practices dispersing its bombers to other bases, making the Kremlin's targeting job far more difficult. During Operation Global Shield, an annual SAC exercise, bombers are rushed aloft at minimum intervals. And how close *is* a minimum interval between B-52s? Distances are not widely publicized but time intervals of twelve seconds have been announced and the public is able to watch on frequent occasions. Says a pilot, "It's the right distance when you can see the glint on the barrel of the tail gun from the guy in front of you."

The Strategic Air Command's B-52 force is spread around Middle America at bases that spring up beside small cities that were once small towns—those tight-knit enclaves of straight and sturdy people who set our values, display our flag, and go off to fight our wars. The locations are mostly far removed from the eastern and western shores of a nation said to be prospering on its two coasts while people struggle in between. The locations may have been *continued on page 48*

B-52s on alert with air-launched cruise missiles. *Jim Benson*

continued from page 47

chosen in part to confound the Kremlin in targeting the US bomber force, but history, happenstance, and no small amount of Congressional politics also determine where our bombers are based.

In Bossier City, Louisiana, they talk about crime, racial tensions and unemployment, and even the City Fathers would acknowledge squalid mobile-home parks, untended used car lots, disorder and ticky-tack within close proximity of neighborhoods exuding genuine southern charm. This is not a city where the Air Force is unwelcome. A B-52 seems veritably to loom over the town as it settles on final approach—but no one minds. Visitors to a local motel, the Sundowner Inn, receive a locally produced *Plane Spotter's Guide* and a message that Bossier is a bird-watcher's paradise. "As long as we hear our planes overhead," concludes the message, "we won't be hearing any enemy's." Thus is the visitor greeted by Barksdale Air Force Base, Louisiana. The base itself—old cavalry horses once grazed there—is pristine and sharp, one of the better-looking bases in the country, kept neat by people with pride.

In Spokane, up in the Pacific Northwest where one learns to live with wet gray murk and even to like it (and "all-weather"

warplanes can only fly ninety-seven percent of the time), the urban clutter and fast-food signs as well as the new, crisp shopping malls belong to a diverse community which is not always mindful of the military but has become accustomed to seeing B-52s overhead. Hobbyists in Spokane have put together a mobile display of scale models of SAC bombers and, with help from civic leaders, it moves to different locations in the region. There is much museum activity in the region where Frederick Johnsen and other historians have restored a B-17. It may be gray and wet, a condition which can become agreeable to the soul, but B-52s are flying on arrival at Fairchild Air Force Base. This bomber installation in the state of Washington is another that has trimmed grass, painted buildings, spit-shined shoes and a look of dedication.

SAC itself is the Air Force's largest command with 121,000 officers, enlisted people and civilians as well as 15,000 SAC-gained reservists. The 260-plane *continued on page 50*

Soaring above the clouds, navigation lights blinking, this B-52 can reach any target in the world. This Stratofortress (60-0042) of the 92nd Bomb Wing is at the pre-contact point on 23 May 1988, waiting to connect with the tanker for an in-flight refueling. *Jim Benson*

continued from page 48
SAC B-52 force is spread within the command's two numbered air forces—the Eighth Air Force at Barksdale under Lieutenant General Ellie G. Shuler, Jr., and the Fifteenth Air Force at March AFB, California, under Lieutenant General Richard A. Burpee.

Within the Eighth Air Force, the units which fly the B-52 include the 2nd, 7th, 42nd, 97th, 379th, 410th and 416th Bomb Wings. The 2nd is at Barksdale; the 7th at Carswell AFB, Texas; the 379th, at Wurtsmith AFB, Michigan; the 410th at K.I. Sawyer AFB, Michigan; the 416th at Griffiss AFB, New York; the 97th at Blythville AFB, Arkansas; the 42nd at Loring AFB, Maine.

In the Fifteenth Air Force's jurisdiction, the Stratofortress is flown by the 5th, 43rd, 92nd, 93rd, and 320th Bomb Wings, located respectively at Minot AFB, North Dakota; Andersen AFB, Guam; Fairchild AFB, Washington; Castle AFB, California; Mather AFB, California.

A SAC press release of 11 May 1988 announced newly-assigned conventional bombing roles for the 43rd Bomb Wing (Andersen), the 62nd Bomb Squadron of the 2nd wing (Barksdale) and the 320th wing (Mather), and the 42nd Wing (Loring).

B-52 Stratofortresses are deployed overseas in small numbers on a regular basis, particularly in connection with their conventional bombing responsibilities. Before the 1988 summer Olympics, a pair of the big bombers made a routine visit to Korea. The increased frequency of such deployments is typified by one unusual event: it was only on 5 August 1987, after more than three decades in service, when a Stratofortress landed on German soil for the very first time. B-52G 59-2601 of the 416th Bomb Wing, stationed at Griffiss AFB, New York, achieved this distinction when it appeared at Ramstein AB, Germany, for *Flugtag,* the annual base open house.

On a combat mission, the 69 B-52G models intended for the conventional mission would carry AGM-84A Harpoon air-to-surface missiles, a new addition to the Stratofortress armory. One squadron of about fifteen aircraft based on Guam conducts this maritime anti-shipping mission in the Pacific while another in Maine does the same job for the Atlantic (both under an Air Force agreement with the Navy). It is understood that Pentagon planners have additional conventional missions in mind for the B-52 as soon as the B-2 Stealth bomber goes into service in the nuclear role in the nineties.

It has been pointed out that B-52s could have been used for the 15 April 1986 air strikes on terrorist-related targets in Libya, taking off and returning from stateside bases, sparing the US any need to use foreign airfields or impinge on any other nation's sovereignty. To make his point that no target anywhere in the world is safe from the B-52, Lieutenant Colonel Lawrence G. Nilssen recalls a B-52 flight when he departed Darwin, Australia, headed up past Diego Garcia into the Arabian Sea, turned around, and (many thousands of miles later) landed in Guam. "Given a choice, we would fly at night and the other guys would have a hell of a time hitting us with anything they might possess—AWACS, infrared missiles, radar-guided missiles, and guns. Because of the tremendous range that we have we can come from a direction that's not expected. The forces which can be brought to bear *immediately* on any point in the globe are about none, except for the B-52."

Nilssen thinks the best quote in support of the B-52 came from the strategic bombing pioneer, General Curtis E. LeMay. The tough, cigar-chewing LeMay put it this way: "Fighters are fun but bombers are *important.*"

Air-to-air refueling was tried on an experimental basis during the Korean War. The Boeing KC-135 Stratotanker here pumping fuel to a Stratofortress is practicing in March 1987 for SAC's intended "Thunderhawks" flight demonstration team, which was to perform refuelings at 500 feet of altitude in front of air show crowds. The proposed demonstrations were called off when KC-135 60-0361 of the 92nd Bomb Wing crashed on 13 March 1987, at Fairchild Air Force Base, Washington, killing all aboard. *Jim Benson*

At Fairchild AFB, Washington, on 24 May 1988, B-52H (61-0028)) of the 92nd Bomb Wing settles down for a landing. "Pattern work," repeatedly taking off and landing at the same airfield, is a must to maintain flying skills but is especially tough on the crew members who don't sit up front. *Jim Benson*

SAC ground crewmen, the bulwark of
the command's fighting force, load
B-61 nuclear bombs aboard a
Stratofortress. This weapon is
prepared for use in a clip of four,
which is hoisted aboard the aircraft
and locked into place. *USAF*

FB-111A in action

In 1969, the US Air Force was in a time of change. Since World War II, the service had been run by "bomber generals," men like General Curtis E. LeMay, General John D. Ryan and General Joseph J. Nazzaro, who were present at the creation of the Air Force and spent their careers in SAC-related assignments. The continued development of new bombers was, to men like these, as certain as sunrise.

But American troop strength in Vietnam was peaking at 550,000, a "fighter mafia" was gaining clout in the Pentagon, and the XB-70 had been wiped out by the advent of the SAM. For the first time, non-SAC officers were rising to lead the Air Force. A new bomber might not, after all, be an inescapable fact of life.

So when the General Dynamics FB-111A came into service amid these changes it was hardly surprising that the "One Eleven" was greeted with a resounding ho-humm.

"Is this all we get?" one bomber man asked.

Not, heaven forbid, that the FB-111A was intended to replace the B-52. It was not. It had shorter range. It carried fewer bombs. It wasn't really "strategic," not in the view of traditionalists.

This new medium-bomber had been selected in 1965 and the Air Force intended to purchase 210 of them, but resistance to the FB-111A arose everywhere—in SAC headquarters at Omaha, in the Pentagon, even among pilots. A review of the program culminated in a March 1969 statement by President Nixon's Defense Secretary, Melvin Laird, that the total "buy" would be sixty aircraft.

In fact, seventy-six airplanes were purchased. Three were used as test articles. A few were operated briefly by the 340th Bomb Wing at Carswell AFB, Texas, conveniently across the aerodrome from the builder's plant. Two SAC bomb wings, the 380th at Plattsburgh AFB, New York, and the 509th at Pease AFB, New Hampshire, still have about 60 FB-111As in service.

It was simple. All of the doubters were dead wrong.

The two-man, variable geometry FB-111A—a cousin to the F-111F fighter-bombers which struck Libya in 1986—can take advantage of air-to-air refueling to go anywhere in the world. Like SAC's other bombers, it can hide in the dirt—flying as low as 300 feet off the ground to confound

continued on page 61

continued from page 59

guns, missiles and MiGs. Participating in the NATO Tiger Meet in Europe, the FB-111A has greatly impressed our allies.

Up where the Adirondack Mountains and Lake Champlain surround Plattsburgh Air Force Base, up there in the "north country" near Interstate I-87 where Clare & Carl's Restaurant serves the locally popular "Michigan" (a chili dog with no beans), and where smokestacks from a paper products mill denote the region's other large employer, Lieutenant Colonel John Plantikow has been wringing out the FB-111A long enough to have accumulated nearly 3,000 hours (to top his 2,200 hours in the B-52). Plantikow confirms that the doubters were wrong.

"If I were going into combat I'd want to do it in a One Eleven. It's the best penetrating aircraft with the best TFR [terrain-*continued on page 66*

Liquidator, alias General Dynamics FB–111A Aardvark (68–0161), apparently the aircraft of Colonel Richard N. Goddard, the wing commander of the 380th Bomb Wing, gets ready for a mission on 31 August 1988. Presumably, no one else will use the red and white wheel chocks emblazoned with the eagle insignia of a full colonel. "You ought to see what we do when the generals come," says a Plattsburgh insider. Presumably, a four-star chock exists for General Jack T. Chain, SAC skipper. *Jim Benson*

FB-111A (68-0258) of the 380th Bomb Wing at Plattsburgh attaches itself to the KC-135 to take on fuel. Initially viewed with some skepticism, the FB-111A has proven itself an effective member of the SAC "big bomber" team. In the nineties, SAC supposedly will lose these very flexible medium bombers, which will be transferred to a tactical role in Europe and given the new designation F-111G. One officer remembers, however, that a similar plan existed in 1976 and never reached fruition. *Jim Benson*

FOXTROT, the Supervisor of Flight (or SOF) performs the "last chance" inspection on General Dynamics FB-111A (68-0271) of the 380th Bomb Wing at Plattsburgh on 31 August 1988. At runway's end, the aircraft commander now has the final decision on whether to commit to the mission. These niceties would be abbreviated or eliminated in a wartime situation. *Jim Benson*

As pilot and navigator go over the checklist together, *Liberty Bell,* or General Dynamics FB-111A (68-0292) is ready to roll, concluding a May 1988 visit to Malmstrom AFB, Montana. The 509th Bomb Wing at Pease AFB, New Hampshire, one of two FB-111A wings in Strategic Air Command, is the same unit that dropped the atomic bombs on Hiroshima and Nagasaki, beginning the heroic and tragic story of "unthinkable" warfare. *Jim Benson*

FB-111A (68-0286) of the 380th
Bomb Wing flies over Maine lakes on
a 30 August 1988 mission from
Plattsburgh Air Force Base. The
current paint scheme for the FB-111A
force is excellent camouflage but poor
cosmetics. Commanders are altering
things by permitting an occasional
touch of color on an aircraft.

Beginning in 1988, FB-111As were
allowed to have nicknames based on
World War II aircraft and crewmen
were allowed to have squadron colors
on helmet visors. Says one, "We used
to have in individualistic scarf and
everything else was Air Force
standard." *Jim Benson*

continued from page 61

following radar]. Its penetration capability is spectacular. I've flown it at 200 feet in the mountains at night at supersonic airspeeds." Plantikow confirms that the FB-111A had stall problems at high angles of attack until 1980 when the entire fleet was fitted with a stall inhibitor system (SIS), which "makes the aircraft a whole lot more friendly."

Because the FB-111A is equipped with an ejection module built by McDonnell Douglas, the cockpit interior is a shirtsleeve environment. Pilot and navigator need not carry parachutes or wear G-suits. The module has a survival kit so there is no need for parkas or other heavy gear. The escape module can also serve as a lifeboat; it is floatable. A pin on the pilot's control stick transforms the stick into a bilge pump!

Parentage of the strategic FB-111A should be attributed to the "fighter" that Defense Secretary Robert S. McNamara wanted in the early sixties, originally called TFX and later F-111. A late blooming and perhaps never fully appreciated design, the tactical F-111 finally achieved success only in the final days of fighting in Southeast Asia (after a disastrous earlier deployment) and later in operations against Libya. The F-111C version was delivered to Australia and an F-111K version

for Britain was canceled; both had the bigger wing which eventually went into the SAC airplane. The prototype of SAC's FB-111A first flew on 30 June 1967.

The FB-111A is powered by two 20,350 lb thrust Pratt & Whitney TF30-P-7 turbofan engines with "triple plow 2" variable intake inlets. It can exceed Mach 2 (1,320 mph) above 30,000 feet in clean condition. The aircraft tips the scales at 119,243 lb when flying fully loaded. It carries 4,673 US gallons of fuel internally and can tote up to 3,000 US gallons in external fuel. In practice, FB-111A operators tend to rely on air-to-air refueling to keep the aircraft "cleaner" than an external fuel load would permit.

Former FB-111A pilot George Larson says that an AWACS or fighter aircraft with ordinary radar won't even see the craft coming, let alone defeat it. "Even if he has Pulse Doppler radar which gives him a look-down/shoot-down capability, when *continued on page 69*

Older style camouflage is seen on FB-111A (69-6504), belonging to the tradition-steeped 509th Bomb Wing at Pease Air Force Base, New Hampshire. Note the smooth camouflage demarcation on the external fuel tank. Readying for takeoff on 26 September 1988, this FB-111A is ready to go and its crew is about to get slammed into the sky by the raw power of the turbofan engines. *Jim Benson*

continued from page 66

he turns it on you're down in the dirt. If he tries to use a radar missile he's got to break us out of ground clutter. If he tries a gun attack, you can go down in the rocks with an FB-111A at night and you've got T/A [terrain avoidance] so he can't get you. His only chance is to make a slashing gun attack coming down at you and he might overshoot. In the FB-111A, you can jink and defeat his bullet flyout time. For the other guy, it's a low percentage shot. . . ."

It is probably true that the FB-111A is extremely difficult, if not impossible, to stop during a treetop-level night or bad-weather attack. Air defenses are almost always over-estimated. The B-52 and B-1B are difficult to stop, too. If the notion of a nuclear bomber racing pell-mell toward a target at high speed and low altitude evokes terrifying visions of a "Dr. Strangelove" world, it must be said in fairness that the men who fly the FB-111A do not like war and do not want to fight one. Says Larson, "No one has ever given me a

continued on page 70

Blatant nudity may have been permitted during World War II but the "nose art" recently authorized for Strategic Air Command aircraft is not likely to offend anyone. *Six bits* is an FB-111A (68-0252) observed on 31 August 1988 at Plattsburgh. *Jim Benson*

continued from page 69

credible argument against readiness."

One conversation with an FB-111A crewman took place on 7 December, Pearl Harbor day. In a nation which admittedly has other problems ranging from the budget deficit to the environment, no one in or out of the FB-111A community has ever given a credible argument in favor of complacency, either. Dollar for dollar, the FB-111A has been a good buy for the taxpayer.

Crew chief on the radar dish of an FB-111A. It's nice work in nice weather but the men and women who stand guard, turn wrenches and repair electronics don't always enjoy warmth and sunlight at bases like Pease and Plattsburgh, and their contribution to the bomber force's readiness often goes unacknowledged. *Jim Benson*

FB-111A (68-0278) nicknamed *A Wing an' Ten Prayers* taxies at Plattsburgh on 31 August 1988. The FB-111A has achieved the best safety record of any aircraft type in service with the US Air Force. When the 100,000 flying-hour mark was reached more than a decade ago, there had been only two serious accidents. The FB-111A frequently steals the show at SAC bombing competitions and the competition between Plattsburgh- and Pease-based aircraft is friendly but fierce. *Jim Benson*

A-turnin' and a-burnin', an FB-111A passes over Plattsburgh on 30 August 1988 on a simulated combat mission. In the mid-sixties, SAC planned to order 210 aircraft plus 65 extras for use as spares to replace 345 B-52C, D and F and 80 B-58A and TB-58 bombers. Despite the spectacular success of the FB-111A, the size of the force was drastically scaled down during the Nixon Administration. FB-111A has a superb mission capable (MC) rate which means, simply, that it works when it's supposed to. *Jim Benson*

74

Who *are* those guys?

A low thin fog blankets the airfield at Barksdale as the KC-10 Extender plows through darkness, heading for runway's end for a pre-dawn launch. Instructor pilot Captain Leeroy A. Martin is so happy to be flying this airplane he can hardly contain himself. He is thirtyish. "At my age, I'd have to wait at least ten years to get into the left-hand seat of a DC-10 airliner," he grins. "I can fly the equivalent aircraft in the Air Force on a tanker/transport mission and help others to learn to fly it." Martin belongs to the Eighth Air Force staff but he likes flying Strategic Air Command's newest tanker much more than his desk.

On a typical mission on 24 October 1988, Martin takes his KC-10 (82-0083) aloft, climbs above the fog, receives fuel from a KC-135R and turns toward the Gulf of Mexico where his boom

Camouflaged Boeing KC-135R Stratotanker (63-8006) of the 319th Bomb Wing taking off at Grand Forks. The new camouflage scheme for tankers makes them *hot:* a KC-135 can reach 130 degrees Fahrenheit inside, basking in the sun. Because of heat damage to electronics, the paint design may not be continued. The much-liked KC-135 tanker dates to the mid-fifties, but the R model is a recent modification with bigger and more powerful CFM56 engines. *Jim Benson*

operator provides fuel to a B-52, a part of the bomber force which would be able to go nowhere, accomplish nothing, without air-to-air refueling. The "guys" who handle the refueling aren't in bombers and don't drop bombs, but no Strategic Air Command would exist without them. Tankers like Martin's are also a part of the backbone of SAC.

"We depend on the tankers for everything," says a B-52 co-pilot. "If we didn't have the KC-135 and KC-10, we would have to invent them. They sustain us. They get us into the mission."

The KC-10 was purchased when the US was developing its Rapid Deployment Joint Task Force in the late seventies. The aircraft was designed to move men and machinery across oceans quickly, ready to fight. In its transport role, the KC-10 can have up to seventy-five seats in addition to its palletized cargo deck which can handle trucks, armored personnel carriers or heavy equipment. While transporting material into a rapidly-unfolding conflict, the KC-10 can refuel anybody who needs it.

Despite its 590,000 lb weight and its enormous looming bulk, the KC-10 is one of the most powerful

continued on page 79

continued from page 77

aircraft ever built. Each of its three General Electric CF6-50C2 turbofan engines generates 52,500 lb of thrust, meaning that a single engine on the KC-10 is more powerful than all four on the KC-135A Stratotanker. On takeoff, the enormous power behind the KC-10 pushes it aloft like a giant space booster. It is literally true that, if other factors did not intervene, its power alone is enough to put the KC-10 into orbit. If a mistake is made in formation flying, the bow wave from a KC-10 can crush a B-52 like an old beer can.

SAC has three squadrons to handle its fifty-nine of these giant aircraft—at March AFB, California; Barksdale AFB, Louisiana; and Seymour Johnson AFB, North Carolina. The *real* mission for which the rapid-deployment KC-10 was intended: rushing a mini-squadron of six jet fighters overseas in the event of a conventional war.

continued on page 80

Wearing blue-white paint as originally delivered (with about half of the fleet likely to remain in these colors), Douglas KC-10 Extender 82-0191 taxies during a stopover at Great Falls International Airport, Montana, on 12 June 1987. In its transport capacity, the KC-10 can use numerous medium airfields around the world. This aircraft belongs to the 32nd Air Refueling Squadron at Barksdale AFB, Louisiana. *Jim Benson*

continued from page 79

To counter a Soviet invasion of the Persian Gulf, the KC-10 could carry all of the men and equipment needed to support the fighters overseas and would refuel the jets while helping them navigate across the ocean. Providing fuel to SAC bombers is but a secondary role, and SAC experts acknowledge that the KC-10 wasn't designed for nuclear war: it lacks thermal flash shields and is not hardened for electromagnetic pulse (EMP) emissions from a nuclear blast.

The standard SAC air-refueling tanker, and the aircraft which *is* hardened for nuclear warfare is the Boeing KC-135 Stratotanker. There were 820 of these four-engine aircraft built and they have become a familiar sight around the world since the prototye for the series was first rolled out on 14 May 1954.

If the KC-135 is to have its proper place in history, it should be recognized as the very first four-engine jet aircraft to attain operational service, and is the progenitor of all the world's jet

KC-10 in flight. This view, on 4 October 1983, depicts aircraft 82-190 which subsequently became the only KC-10 to be lost in an accident, in a fire at Barksdale on 17 September 1987. The KC-10 has, in fact, had an exemplary flight safety record and is considered relatively easy to fly despite its enormous size. *Lindsay T. Peacock*

airliners, transports and tankers. The myth still persists in many quarters that the familiar KC-135 is, in fact, a military version of the Boeing 707 jetliner. It is not. The KC-135 is a different aircraft and came ahead of the 707 by a considerable amount of time. The boldness of the Air Force in investing in a jet-powered tanker fleet helped to make the subsequent airline fleet possible.

The KC-135 has been proven to be one of the most versatile airplanes in history and versions of it are used for everything from reconnaissance to zero-G flight trials for Space Shuttle astronauts. The basic SAC tanker version remains the most important and most numerous. Principal versions are the KC-135A (the original aircraft, with Pratt & Whitney J57 turbojets), KC-135E (with TF33 turbofan engines) and KC-135R (with newer, "fat" CFM56 powerplants), as well as a
continued on page 86

Not every recipient of fuel belongs to SAC. Connected to the boom of Captain Martin's KC-10 Extender 83-0082 on 24 October 1988 is a Tactical Air Command EC-130E Hercules airborne command post (62-1836) of the 7th Airborne Command & Control Squadron at Keesler AFB, Mississippi. Even Staff Sergeant Sara Galvin, a crew member of the EC-130E, acknowledges that her aircraft lacks color. Fortunately, a KC-10 bumper sticker displayed on the windshield adds a touch of red and blue. *Robert F. Dorr*

KC-10 pilot at work. Captain Leeroy
A. Martin of the Eighth Air Force
staff pilots KC-10 Extender 83-0082
over the Gulf of Mexico on 24
October 1988. *Robert F. Dorr*

SAC people. Following a 24 October 1988 combat support mission in KC-10 Extender (83-0082), callsign ELITE 28, of the 32nd Air Refueling Squadron, the augmented crew of the tanker/transport assembles at Barksdale AFB, Louisiana. Standing (left to right) are Captain Lanny J. Morris, co-pilot; Captain Leeroy A. Martin, instructor pilot; TSGT Letch J. Chadwell, flight engineer; SMSGT George H. Ellison, flight engineer; Captain Michael G. Padgett, pilot. Kneeling (left to right) are TSGT Dennis C. Fox and TSGT Richard W. Otis, boom operators. *Robert F. Dorr*

At Minot Air Force Base, North Dakota, on 18 August 1988, a half-dozen KC-135s and B-52s line up, showing two paint schemes for each type of aircraft. For the inveterate tail number buff, it was noted that the Stratofortresses of the 5th Bomb Wing are 60-0061, 61-0005 and 61-0002. Minot looks pleasant in this busy view. In winter, however, Minot is just plain cold. For those who need the challenge of city life, this quote from a B-52 pilot, "You have a town of 45,000 people nearby. But if you get bored, it's no problem. You get on the road and drive two hours and you'll reach *another* town of 45,000 people." *Jim Benson*

Douglas KC-10 Extender (84-0129) of the 22nd Air Refueling Squadron based at March AFB, California, makes a stop at Fairchild AFB, Washington, on 24 May 1988. *Jim Benson*

continued from page 81

KC-135Q variant which is used solely to refuel the SR-71, U-2 and TR-1 reconnaissance aircraft. SAC has about 325 KC-135A, 125 KC-135E, 100 KC-135R and 50 KC-135Q aircraft. Twenty-four of the E models are operated by dedicated Air Force Reserve units. The Air Natonal Guard also has KC-135Es.

At first glance, in-flight refueling looks incredibly risky. After all, tanker and receiver are flying along at high speed while holding formation within a few feet of each other. They must be prepared to alter flight path or break away if circumstances require.

The bomber crews who depend on refueling will be first to acknowledge tanker people are not just "bus drivers," not second fiddle in any way when it comes to being ready to carry out a bombing mission accomplishing the mission in the best way. On a 10,000 mile journey to a distant strategic target, a B-52 might need to take on fuel as many as five times, depending on the mission profile. Some or all of the refueling mission may have to be carried out on short notice, in bad weather, under pressure, at the fringes of enemy territory.

Neither the KC-135 nor the KC-10 is difficult to fly. Both, in fact, are remarkably forgiving aircraft which can hum like a fine tune in the hands of an expert and

86

tolerate the heavy touch of the inexperienced. Both have their peculiarities, however, and they require in their own ways just as much skill and dedication as do bombers.

The KC-10, for example, is very difficult to taxi. In his left-hand cockpit seat, the pilot has no references. He cannot see his own wing. His nose wheel is far behind him. In his far-forward perch, the pilot could easily be overlooking the farm next door to the airbase while, far behind him, the nose wheel is steering correctly. In tight spaces, the pilot must suffer the indignity of asking the boom operator to look out the back door and say whether he's about to clip a wingtip.

The KC-135 is extremely stable in level flight but is not an easy aircraft to land, especially when bloated with fuel, and many a new pilot has made a "go around" rather than miss the necessary three-pointer. The boom oprator in the KC-135 must continued on page 90

Strategic Air Command tankers spent a considerable portion of their time refueling fighters. In March 1985 near the flight test center at Edwards AFB, California, KC-135 Stratotanker (61-0315) refuels F-4D Phantom (66-7483) of the 6512th Test Squadron, piloted by Captain Guy Walsh. Daylight refueling is not easy, but tanker crews must also be ready to do it in the dark, in bad weather, under fire.

A typical recipient of air-to-air refueling is this B-52H Stratofortress approaching a KC-135 tanker high over Idaho. *Jim Benson*

B-52 Stratofortress taking on fuel. *Jim Benson*

Next page
The ever-essential ground crews, the people who keep 'em flying, look over a camouflaged Douglas KC-10 Extender at March AFB, California, which is one of three SAC bases operating the latest tanker/transport. Sixty of these aircraft, based on the DC-10 widebody jetliner, were ordered in the late seventies to support the Carter-era Rapid Deployment Force. *USAF*

continued from page 86

recline, prone, on his or her belly while refueling another aircraft. In the KC-10, at least, comfortable chairs as well as the largest window aboard any aircraft are provided to the boomer.

If a future exists for the SAC bomber force, in a kind of warfare where a large, unarmed aircraft can become a target even over its home base, the twenty-first century replacement for the KC-135 and KC-10 may need to be some form of "stealth" tanker. Already, planners are looking at new design features, similar to those in the Northrop B-2 bomber, which would render a tanker less vulnerable to detection by an enemy. Any such development lies far in the future, however. In a time of major budget constraints, the SAC tanker force is one item that isn't broke and doesn't need to be fixed.

But even if SAC's tanker crews go aloft in a flying saucer, the role of every one of the crew members will remain critical, especially the role (sorry, sir!) of the boom operator. The others in the tankers will continue to be a vital part of Strategic Air Command's bomber team.

Enter the B-1B

"The world's first self-jamming bomber," sneers a Washington journal. The Rockwell B-1B Excalibur bomber is possibly the most maligned and misunderstood warplane ever to come down the pike. Even its nickname never caught on, mostly because a condom manufacturer used it first. Canceled by Jimmy Carter, rescued by Ronald Reagan, the B-1B is depicted by its opponents as too late, too costly and totally unnecessary.

Somehow, however, B-1B crews love their aircraft and Air Force Chief of Staff General Larry D. Welch calls it the best bomber in the world today. The most important criticism of the aircraft, that its defensive electronic system doesn't work as advertised, is only partly true. "As bad as the defensive system is reputed to be," says B-1B pilot Captain M. P.

From a distance, the B-1B could possibly be mistaken for a fighter, but when it passes overhead the sheer size of the bomber becomes apparent. This B-1B (86-0111) of the 319th Bomb Wing demonstrates the swept-forward configuration of the variable-geometry wing for low-speed flight during landings and takeoffs. With FB-111A and B-1B, the US Air Force is in the unique position of having variable-geometry wings on two of its three bombers. *Jim Benson*

Curphey, "it is much better than what came before it. It is *not* just useless weight sitting there doing nothing. The system *does* work but it takes less automation and more human input.

"Why the B-1B? You can't fly thirty-year-old B-52s forever. Small items, generators, parts and such, in the B-52 were built by people no longer in business. Should we have bought the B-1B? Yes. It has a lesser radar signature. It carries a conventional load equal to the Big Belly mods on the B-52 plus anything in the nuclear inventory. And consider the cost of training the crew. With the B-1B you go from a crew of seven or eight to a crew of only four. The cost of maintenance is lower, the size of a maintenance force is lower. All these savings translate downstream as lower costs per airplane."

In fact, the B-1B may be the first Stealth bomber, well ahead of the Northrop B-2. The fuselage blends into the wing, creating a low-drag configuration. The B-1B has been reported in aviation literature to have a radar cross-section (RCS) only one-fourth that of the B-52. An Air Force release says the RCS is 1/100th that of a B-52. Unlike the B-52, the B-1B

continued on page 97

An early developmental B-1B aircraft (actually a modified B-1A latches on to the boom of a KC-135 tanker from the Maine Air National Guard. The camouflage paint scheme and the shape of the nose-mounted canard wing surfaces are the features most noticeable about this aircraft, which differ from the configuration of the production B-1B. *USAF*

B-1B bomber (86-0118) in flight over the northern United States. The pattern of white lines criss-crossing the nose is intended to guide the boom operator of a tanker aircraft in refueling the bomber. The B-1B is reported to have markedly greater range than the B-52 but must still rely upon in-flight refueling to complete its mission. *Jim Benson*

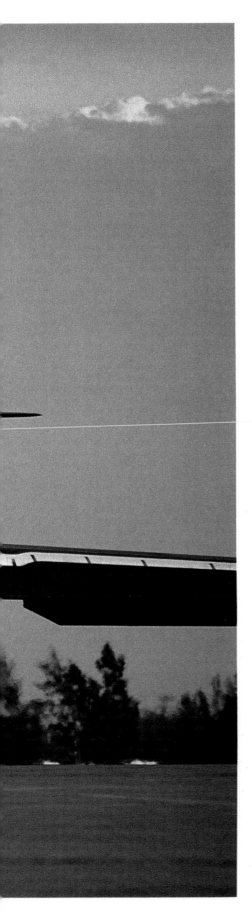

continued from page 93
was built from the outset to go into combat at treetop altitude. The B-1B is faster than other bombers, harder to find, harder to hit.

From the viewpoint of dollar signs, the $282 million B-1B—probably no more than what it would cost to build a B-52 in today's dollars—is not only less expensive to operate than other bombers, it is also less expensive to operate than critics assert. As a contemporary design, the B-1B has "modular maintainability," so to speak—its innards comprise line replaceable units (LRU) which save on mechanic diagnostic time.

Operational advantages of the B-1B are highly appealing to crews. Says Curphey, "You can start engines and scramble faster. The B-1B has a smaller footprint [aircraft weight on tire surfaces] so you can disperse to more alternate airbases."

SAC's commander-in-chief General John T. (Jack) Chain, Jr., told the *Columbus Despatch* that it angers him when the American people are not being told the truth, and that the story of the B-1B

Rockwell B-1B bomber (86-0113) of the 319th Bomb Wing taxies out for an evening flight at Grand Forks AFB, North Dakota, on 15 August 1988. For modeling buffs, the color schemes now employed on SAC bombers consist of two shades of dark gray (federal standards FS 36081 and 36118) and one of dark green (FS 34086). *Jim Benson*

bomber is a good example. General Chain pointed out that the press reported the B-1B to have fuel leaks, but failed to note that fuel leaks never jeopardized the ability of the plane to perform its mission and, in any event, had been corrected.

The SAC chief also pointed out that some 8,000 lb had been intentionally added to the basic airframe of the B-1B by beefing up the structure so as to add 50,000 lb more bombs and 24,000 lb more fuel. Far from correctly reporting that the combat capability of the B-1B had been enhanced, the press charged that the airplane was overweight.

The roster of charges goes on. It is a myth, Chain insists, that the B-1B's terrain-following radar doesn't work. In fact, there was a software problem which was rectified.

As this volume went to press, the B-1B remained a controversy in some quarters, but General Chain and others had made a serious effort to tell the favorable side of the bomber's story. On one occasion, Air Force Chief of Staff General Larry D. Welch met with the Pentagon news corps and granted an in-depth interview on the B-1B, but not a single article followed. On another occasion, a twenty-two-minute speech by General Larry Skantze at the National Press Club was barely

continued on page 98

continued from page 97

reported at all. Even when media representatives visited Dyess Air Force Base and looked at the B-1B, guided by candid crews who reported their views accurately, news stories "trashed" the bomber—Chain's verb. Even the B-1B's strongest advocates agree that the B-1B has some faults. But even some of the bomber's strongest critics have acknowledged that the trashing has gotten way out of hand.

B-1B Excalibur crews will be the first to point out that their aircraft has attained its full specified range capability, which is considerably greater than that of the B-52. It carries a substantially larger bomb load which it delivers with much improved accuracy.

As for the oft-reiterated "self-jamming" claim, one of the most challenging aspects of the B-1B program is the AN/ALQ-161 defensive avionics system. This electronic warfare system built by *continued on page 101*

Afterburners roar to life creating a blazing fire in the exhaust of the giant engines of B-1B 86-0113 at Grand Forks on 15 August 1988. As impressive as the sight is, even small fighters have larger exhaust plumes than the B-1B. In developing the F-101-GE-102 turbofan engine, General Electric made the powerplant "neutral" as to location, so that any individual engine can be installed on either side of either nacelle. *Jim Benson*

continued from page 98
the Eaton Corporation is a state-of-the-art system that includes 108 plug-in boxes and a myriad of antennas and jamming transmitters. It is designed to detect enemy targets and direct electronic countermeasures. In a public statement, the Pentagon acknowledged, "Some of the responses of the 161 are exactly what we had asked for and are working well. In other areas, particularly against the newer threats that didn't even exist at the time we went on contract the 161 is working less well." The statement added, "We bit off a lot technologically and this mouthful will take a little more time to chew."

The B-1B is powered by four 30,000 lb thrust augmented General Electric F101-GE-102 turbofan engines. It carries a crew of four: aircraft commander, co-pilot and offensive and defensive systems operators. An interesting point is that, like many new aircraft including the KC-10, it does not require a navigator.
continued on page 102

B-1B bomber crew at work. The no-nonsense cockpit layout is sensible and functional. Considering their responsibilities, the pilots are actually burdened with relatively few flight controls to handle and monitor. Pilots report that the B-1B is a pleasure to fly. *USAF*

continued from page 101

Its variable geometry or "swing" wing will give the B-1B greater pre-launch survivability because it can get airborne faster than the B-52. At low speeds (takeoffs and landings) the B-1B's wings will be placed in the full-forward position because a straight wing is far more effective at slow speeds than a swept wing. Wing span is 137 feet at a sweep of 15 degrees, 78 feet at 67.5 degrees. An Air Force release quotes the maximum operating weight of the aircraft as 477,000 lb and the bombload as 125,000 lb.

The B-1B impresses people as a black, brooding piece of machinery, as sinister as the horrors of nuclear war for which it was designed. No one who flies the aircraft likes war. All are serious men who see their duty as deterrence. But this does not prevent the B-1B pilot from seeing his aircraft as the real-life embodiment of all that's new and exciting about hi-tech and about flying.

Most of the pilots flying the B-1B are former B-52 pilots, although a few have come from the FB-111A and KC-135 communities and one or two have other backgrounds. The typical pilot is very experienced and is at least a captain or major by the time he becomes aircraft commander of a B-1B. Beginning in 1988, General Chain authorized

putting into the B-1B new pilots who are starting out in their first operational aircraft type.

The B-1B dispensed with a feature standard on the FB-111A and tried out on the B-1A test airplanes: an encapsulated escape system. This would have enabled the crew to work in shirtsleeves and eject as part of a module lowered to earth by its own parachutes. The crew of the B-1B sit in Douglas-designed, Weber-built ACES II (Advanced Concept Ejection Seats) with the parachute and individual oxygen supply stowed aboard the seat itself.

There's a camaraderie among the crew. There has to be. In other commands, crews don't fly together all the time but in SAC airmen work, fly, live and play together. Pilot and co-pilot sit side-by-side and have an instrument panel which includes a mixture of digital and analog instruments, and several cathode-ray terminals. The B-1B is flown much like a fighter, using stick and rudder pedals. It has been pointed out that the B-1B lacks a head-up display, which has proven effective on some tactical aircraft, but for the low-level mission which relies so heavily on continued on page 106

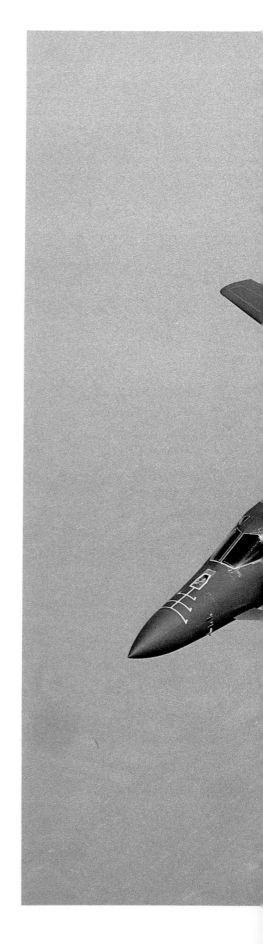

B-1B bomber (86-0118) in flight. Wings remain forward-swept at the angle employed for takeoffs and landings. *Jim Benson*

Nighttime flight line view of B-1B
bomber (86-0111) of the 319th Bomb
Wing at Grand Forks AFB, North
Dakota, on 15 August 1988. Bathed
in floodlights, this aircraft is not going
anywhere at the moment, but bomber
crews do practice their missions at
night and in bad weather. *Jim Benson*

B-1B bomber gets a taste of artifically-induced arctic weather at the climate chamber at Eglin Air Force Base, Florida. The Air Force must test new aircraft under a variety of conditions to determine suitability in all temperatures and conditions. Since the US-Soviet confrontation will most likely occur over northerly climes, it is especially important for the bomber to be able to operate when fleece-lined jackets and long woolies are in order out of doors. *Jim Benson*

continued from page 102

terrain-following technology this feature really is unnecessary.

Offensive and defensive systems operators sit side-by-side behind the pilots and face forward although they do not have much of a view outside the aircraft. The former's job is to get the aircraft to the target and release the ordnance at the right time. The latter operates the much-publicized AN/ALQ-161 defensive system. Unlike the B-52 which retains tail armament, the B-1B carries no guns.

B-1B bombers serve with these bomb wings: 28th at Ellsworth AFB, South Dakota; 96th at Dyess AFB, Texas; 319th at Grand Forks, North Dakota; and 384th at McConnell AFB, Kansas.

Some B-1B crew members have asserted that the ideal B-1B flier is the youngster who liked to tinker a lot, who has in him the soul of an inventor, the curiosity of a scientist. Others say the airplane is right for the natural pilot who has a "seat-of-the-pants" instinct for his work. With the 100th and last B-1B bomber—rolled off the final assembly line on 20 January 1988, six years to the day of the signing of development and production contracts—the sleek black bomber is now a vital part of the US bomber force and an important deterrent for the future.

Previous page
B-1B bomber of the 96th Bomb Wing stationed at Dyess AFB, Texas, performs a tight turn with moisture clouds coming back from the wings on 10 March 1987. This Aircraft is being flown by instructor pilot Major James P. Robinson. *USAF/TSGT Jose Lopez*

B-1B bomber pulls up over the southwestern American desert. Co-pilot Captain Michael E. Waters may be at the controls now. 96th Bomb Group at Dyess routinely practices over the broad expanses in Arizona and New Mexico. *USAF/TSGT Jose Lopez*

Keeping the peace

It is a dark, wet, rainy morning at Castle AFB just outside Merced, California. The golden sun so typical of the area got lost in murk today. On the 93rd Bomb Wing's flight line, the snap and whine of engines beginning to turn is a sure sign that the Buffs are coming to life.

From certain angles, the long line of bombers parked on the ramp seems to stretch to infinity. From a distance, it is hard to distinguish which aircraft, or even how many, have started up.

After a decent interval for the crew to hunker down and be settled in their tasks, a tail begins slowly to move out of its place in the lineup of aircraft. Like the fin of a shark, slicing along against a still background. Soon, another. And another. Falling into position, bomber after bomber begin their slow lumbering pace to the hammerhead, their wings sagging, their landing lights reflecting off the wet concrete beneath them.

The bomber of the future, the Air Force says. The Northrop B-2 flying wing Stealth bomber, designed to elude enemy radar. The two-man bomber was shown to the public on 22 November 1988, when it had not yet flown and seemed, at the time, years away from becoming an operational part of Strategic Air Command. *USAF*

At the hammerhead (the turn-around by runway's end), the supervisor of flight (SOF), callsign FOXTROT, waits in his vehicle for the lead bomber to give him the go-ahead to start his last-chance inspection. The task has been performed hundreds of times before but each time it is serious, thorough. FOXTROT is usually a pilot and he draws this additional duty about twice a month. Next time, he may be in the cockpit and today's pilot on the ground.

The first B-52 settles to a halt, a temporary halt while looking as if it intends to lunge into the sky. The pilot clears FOXTROT for his last-chance check. "FOX, This is CZAR 01, you're cleared in. Brakes are locked. Radar's down."

FOXTROT acknowledges and begins to slowly circle the huge bomber, looking for anything that might present a hazard to aircraft or crew. Oil, hydraulic leaks, unpulled pins—anything. He makes certain the giant flaps of the Stratofortress are in their correct position.

When FOXTROT is satisfied that the aircraft is safe, he calls to CZAR 01. "01, FOX. Confirm, you are in takeoff configuration. Have a good flight."

continued on page 116

Flaps down, lights on, outrigger wheels riding high, B-52H Stratofortress of the 92nd Bomb Wing at Fairchild AFB, Washington, on 24 May 1988 could be coming or going from a simulated combat mission. Many generations of aircrews have passed since the Stratofortress became the principal American bomber and it remains, today, the principal warplane in the American bomber force. It is a magnificent aircraft with a record of achievement almost impossible to quantify. *Jim Benson*

A Wing An' 10 Prayers, alias General Dynamics FB-111A 68-0278 of the 380th Bomb Wing, seemingly ready for Captain Tom McAusland to take it aloft, sits in a sea of fuel and hydraulic leakage, where aircraft parking slots are marked by oily black residue. Some FB-111A crews pooh-pooh the notion that their stateside aircraft will soon be reassigned to Europe, pointing out that they've heard the story before. *Jim Benson*

113

FB-111A launch. *Jim Benson*

Heading toward the mission are
B-1B bombers 60-0110 and 60-0111
at Grand Forks on 16 August 1988.
On this occasion, the departure of the
two bombers from their parking slot
was delayed by repairs to an oxygen
system. The 300 mm lens compacts
the image and makes it look as if the
second bomber is right behind the first
but in fact the two B-1Bs were more
than 200 feet apart. The second plane
must remain some distance back or its
air intakes swallow up FOD (foreign
object damage) from tiny items on the
runway kicked up by the first. *Jim
Benson*

114

continued from page 111

FOXTROT moves on to check the next bomber which is stopped directly behind the lead, just out of reach of the engines' jet wash.

Today, three B-52s and a single tanker will make up the early morning launch from Castle. This will be a simulated alert launch. The takeoff will be a MITO (minimum interval takeoff), with the spacing of aircraft to be twelve seconds. The Director of Operations (DO) for the 93rd Bomb Wing is always on hand for a MITO, and he will give the execution authorization to the command post when satisfied that safety requirements have been met.

When all checks are complete, the pilot of 01 inches the throttles forward and the aircraft moves slowly to the hold line, a bright yellow strip that separates the hammerhead from the active runway. Navigators like to cross the hold line "on the hack."

Once the lead bomber crosses the hold line, the Stratofortresses do not stop but turn onto the runway and begin their takeoff rolls. As the lead bomber lifts off they will point their aircraft to the north.

Twelve seconds later, CZAR 02 will be off the ground, heading slightly left of the lead's jet wash.

Fourteen seconds later, CZAR 03 is lurching off the runway and no matter what the lead and second aircraft have done, CZAR 03 is going to have a rocky few seconds. It is not uncommon for the last ship to be in a left bank turn, even though the pilot is initiating full right yoke and full right rudder.

Because of the performance differences between the B-52 Stratofortress and the KC-135 Stratotanker, the tanker will have a thirty-second spacing after the last Buff.

In wartime, the bombers would have come not from the flight line but from the heavily-guarded alert complex where B-52s are kept cocked and ready to respond at a moment's notice. The safety procedures might have been eliminated or abbreviated, in time of conflict.

But it is not wartime. People who fly the bombers know why. It rings hollow. It sounds corny. It does not fit in today's "me first" era—when most of us, from *continued on page 118*

The Baroness, better known on the charts as Boeing B-52H Stratofortress 60-0016, is ready for a mission at Minot AFB, North Dakota, on 18 August 1988. Nose art is a recent phenomenon in SAC but crews appreciate the opportunity to put individual markings on their aircraft. *Baroness* belongs to the 5th Bomb Wing. *Jim Benson*

continued from page 116

corporate boardroom to crackhouse basement, are bent on self; when most of us are, in fact, preoccupied with the price of everything except the price of freedom. It sounds hollow and corny but at SAC bases, in the separate society of those who bear arms, men and women remain who are unashamed of the words duty, honor, country.

It is not wartime because the Strategic Air Command bomber force has prevented war.

The Strategic Air Command bomber force consists of the B-52 Stratofortress, the FB-111A and the B-1B. It may, in the nineties, include Northrop B-2 Stealth bombers which the Air Force says will be stationed at Whiteman Air Force Base, Missouri. But in a time of conflicting demands on a nation's priorities, only President Bush himself will be able to decide whether SAC will receive all of the 132 B-2 bombers it wants. Unveiled on 22 November 1988, to the strains of a musical work entitled *Stealth Fanfare*, the B-2 is not yet a part of the Strategic Air Command and, thus, not a part, not yet, of our story.

continued on page 122

B-1B bomber over the Rocky Mountains. *USAF/TSGT Jose Lopez*

A slightly off-balance Aardvark on a rehearsal mission above the southwestern corner of Vermont, in the dark paint scheme rapidly becoming standard for the FB-111A. The navigator in the right-hand seat of the FB-111A is at times jokingly referred to as a YOT ("you over there"). Elsewhere in the Air Force, navigator slots are becoming fewer and fewer. Even the SAC B-1B and KC-10 fly without "navs," but at Pease and Plattsburgh Air Force Bases, the second man's skill remains vital. *Jim Benson*

B-52H Stratofortress 61-0028, another aircraft belonging to the 92nd Bomb Wing at Fairchild AFB, Washington, but here exemplifying all B-52s of all units, comes down for a landing and extends its braking parachute. The successful completion of a flight always marks an important ending for an aircrew, but the job isn't over until the paperwork is done and the post-mission debriefing (including a safety portion aimed at analyzing anything that wasn't right) may continue for some time. *Jim Benson*

continued from page 118

The crews who must be ready to fly and fight aboard B-52, FB-111A and B-1B, as well as the aircrews who make up the tanker force, are far from blind to the future. They await the B-2 as eagerly as any teenage modeler. But you cannot fight, cannot win, with an aircraft on the drawing board. Too often, the mistake is made of talking about our capabilities in the context of experimental aircraft under test, rather than the harsh reality of the operator's world. If we have to fight and win tomorrow morning, the operators of the SAC bomber force—the big bombers—will do the job with what they have today, here, now.

There used to be signs at Air Force bases, reminding those in shade 84 blue uniforms, "THE MISSION OF THE UNITED STATES AIR FORCE IS TO FLY AND FIGHT AND DON'T YOU EVER FORGET IT."

There used to be signs at Strategic Air Command bases, telling the world "PEACE IS OUR PROFESSION."

The words are corny. The words are wooden. In an era of self-interest, when we are divided as countrymen, no one really knows whether Americans still possess the will to employ force of arms if the need arises. The supreme paradox is, only the willingness to think about it will prevent the unthinkable. Only readiness to fight will make it unnecessary to fight.

A junior airman tried to warn General Curtis E. LeMay not to suck on his cigar while standing next to a tanker, lest cinders cause the aircraft to explode. LeMay snapped, "It wouldn't dare!" Modesty is not a quality that molds a strategic force, and hesitance is not a virtue in the bomber business. The people in our nation's force of big bombers do keep the peace. As long as they stay on the job, keeping the bombers and tankers at the ready, no others, anywhere, will be able to hurl us into an unthinkable war.

They wouldn't dare, either.

All manner of yellow-hosed gadgetry is needed to pump frigid air into the B-1B Excalibur bomber (to keep the electronics cool) this example being aircraft 60-0113 of the 319th Bomb Wing at Grand Forks on 16 August 1988. The crew chief who latches the bomber to its umbilical has a personal commitment to the success of the dark, sharply pointed aircraft. Despite critics, the B-1B has a good safety record and excellent statistics on the completion of simulated combat missions. *Jim Benson*

Manhandling the bombs, the heavy bombs that are often carried externally on a conventional mission, never gets easier. B-52H Stratofortress 61-0002, or *Balls Two* to use the slang term for its serial number's zeroes, will soon be "bombed up" and ready to go. *Jim Benson*

It always is, always was, the B-52. In the foreground is B-52H Stratofortress 60-0058 of the 92nd Bomb Wing heading up a row of bombers which look ready and carry air-launched cruise missiles. A significant number of the men who fly in the B-52 were born after the first Stratofortress made its maiden flight, but the B-52 remains the most numerous of Strategic Air Command's big bombers. Not just an aircraft, more a national treasure, the B-52 will be in service for the foreseeable future. *Jim Benson*

B-1B bomber 60-0118 moving up on
the tanker to receive fuel high over the
northern United States. *Jim Benson*